MW00414215

The
Fun
Book
of
Bible
Trivia **2**

The Fun Book of Bible Trivia 2

Robyn Martins

A BARBOUR BOOK

Published by Barbour and Company, Inc.
            P.O. Box 719
            Uhrichsville, OH 44683

Printed in the United States of America

IT'S A TRIVIAL THING

Judah had as many gods as they did towns.
Jeremiah 11:13

When the Lord opened the seventh seal in John's vision, all
of heaven was quiet for about half an hour.
Revelation 8:1

God smelled Noah's burnt offering after the flood.
Genesis 8:21

Isaiah said, "The Lord will whistle for flies from Egypt and
bees from Assyria." Picture it. Isaiah 7:18

Solomon's girlfriend had to take care of the vineyards
because her brothers were mad at her. Solomon 1:6

Some descendants of priests couldn't find their family
records, so they weren't allowed to be priests. Unclean!
Ezra 1:62

Abraham's father Terah died in Haran. Haran was the
name of Terah's son who died in Ur. Genesis 11:28, 32

Esther was given seven maids even before she was made the queen. Esther 2:9

When Nehemiah found out that some Hebrew men had married foreign women, he beat them and pulled out their hair. Nehemiah 13:25

John wrote the book of Revelation to seven churches in Asia. Revelation 1:4

When Jesus drove out a mute demon from a mute man, the man was able to speak. Luke 11:14

The Lord used the king of Assyria as a razor to shave the legs of the people of Judah. Isaiah 7:20

King Nebuchadnezzar made Daniel chief of magicians, enchanters, astrologers, and diviners. Daniel 5:11

A man named Simon tried to pay Peter and John for the power to give people the Holy Spirit. Acts 8:19

Zechariah saw a vision of a woman trapped in a basket that was carried away by two women with wings. Zechariah 5:6-9

The Lord showed Amos a bowl full of ripe fruit—ripe like Israel was for judgment. Amos 8:1-2

WAS IT "PSALM"-THING I SAID?

David had a way with words. Fill in the missing ones in this quiz from the Psalms.

1. Their throat is an _____ _____, with their tongue they speak deceit.

2. Oh Lord, our Lord, how majestic is _____ _____.

3. . . .My God is my rock in whom _____ _____ _____.

4. Remember not the sins of _____ _____.

5. The voice of the Lord is _____; the voice of the Lord is _____.

6. _____and see that the Lord is good.

7. Sing to the Lord a _____ _____, for he has done marvelous _____.

8. They repay me evil for _____, and hatred for my _____.

9. I lift up my eyes to the _____—where does my _____ come from?

10. Your word, O Lord, is _____; it stands firm in the _____.

ANSWERS

1. open grave. 5:9

2. your name. 8:1

3. I take refuge. 18:2

4. my youth. 25:6

5. powerful, majestic. 29:4

6. taste. 34:8

7. new song, things. 98:19

8. good, friendship. 109:5

9. hills, help. 121:1

10. eternal, heavens. 119:89

 Who killed Jonathan, Saul's son?

The Philistines. 1 Chronicles 10:2.

WHO SAID?

1. "Give me wisdom and knowledge, that I may lead this people..."

2. "Am I a dog that you come at me with sticks?"

3. "Whom are you pursuing? A dead dog? A flea?"

4. "When will you end these speeches? Be sensible, and then we can talk."

5. "You are a child of the devil; and an enemy of every thing that is right."

6. "Don't be afraid, for I will surely show you kindness for the sake of your father Jonathan."

7. "O Lord, my God, have you brought tragedy also upon this widow I am staying with by causing her son to die?"

8. "My father! My father! The chariots and horsemen of Israel."

9. "Worthy is the Lamb who was slain, to receive power and wealth and wisdom and strength and honor and glory and praise."

10. "Naked I came from my mother's womb, and naked I will depart."

ANSWERS

1. Solomon. 2 Chronicles 1:10

2. Goliath. 1 Samuel 17:43

3. David to Saul. 1 Samuel 24:14

4. Bildad to Job. Job 18:2

5. Paul. Acts 13:10

6. David to Mephibosheth. 2 Samuel 9:7

7. Elijah. 1 Kings 17:20

8. Elisha. 2 Kings 2:116

9. More angels than John could count. Revelation 5:12

10. Job. Job 1:21

SACKCLOTH IS IN

King Hezekiah tore his clothes and put on sackcloth and went into the temple. Isaiah 37:1

The king of Nineveh put it on and sat in the dust. He even covered his animals with it. Jonah 3:6-7

David said, "I put on sackcloth and humbled myself with fasting." Psalm 35:13

Mordecai put it on when he found out that Haman ordered all the Jews to be killed. Esther 4:1

Jacob put on sackcloth when he thought Joseph had been eaten by an animal. Genesis 37:34

Job wore sackcloth during his time of torment. Job 16:15

In Jeremiah's day, people put scarecrows in melon patches.
Jeremiah 10:5

A rainbow surrounded a throne in heaven while John was
watching "in the spirit." Revelation 4:13

Ham was the father of Canaan. Genesis 9:18

John ate a scroll that was as sweet as honey but made his
stomach sour. Well, of course. Revelation 10:10

> **?** Who said, "I know where you live"?
> Revelation 2:13
> Jesus, about the church in Pergamum.

The two days of Purim are celebrated to recall the
Hebrew's victorious two-day battle against enemies while
Esther was queen. Esther 9:18-28

Every morning Job sacrificed a burnt offering just in case
one of his children had sinned. What a dad! Job 1:5

David had 20 children. 1 Chronicles 3:1-9

AND GOD SAID. . .

"let there be light" and many other things. List the results of God's creation in order of their occurrence.

1.

2.

3.

4.

5.

6.

7.

ANSWERS

Genesis 1:1-1:2

1. On the first day, God created light.

2. On the second day, God separated land from water.

3. On the third day, God created vegetation.

4. On the fourth day, God created the sun, moon, and stars.

5. On the fifth day, God created marine life and birds.

6. On the sixth day, God created land animals and people.

7. On the seventh day, God created rest.

AND THEN GOD SAID

To whom was God speaking when He said. . .

1. "As long as the earth endures, seedtime and harvest, cold and heat, summer and winter, day and night will never cease."

2. "Son of man, tremble as you eat your food, and shudder in fear as you drink your water."

3. "Can you pull in the leviathan with a fishhook or tie down his tongue with a rope?"

4. "With the three hundred men that lapped I will save you and give the Midianites into your hands."

5. "See, I am about to do something in Israel that will make the ears of everyone who hears of it tingle."

6. "Take again the equipment of a foolish shepherd."

7. "Get up and go into Damascus. There you will be told all that you have been assigned to do."

8. "I will have mercy on whom I will have mercy, and I will have compassion on whom I will have compassion."

9. "You will shepherd my people Israel, and you will become their ruler."

10. "I have seen this people, and they are a stiff-necked people indeed."

ANSWERS

1. Noah. Genesis 8:22

2. Ezekiel. Ezekiel 12:18

3. Job. Job 41:2

4. Gideon. Judges 7:7

5. Samuel. 1 Samuel 3:11

6. Zechariah. Zechariah 11:15

7. Paul. Acts 22:10

8. Moses. Exodus 33:19

9. David. 2 Samuel 5:2

10. Moses. Deuteronomy 9:13

WHEN FOOLS RUSH IN

Wise sayings about the foolish.

A fool will be a servant to the wise. Proverbs 11:29

A fool exposes his folly. Proverbs 4:16

It's better to meet a bear robbed of her cubs than one.
Proverbs 17:12

To have one for a son brings grief. Proverbs 17:21

When one speaks a proverb, it's like a lame man's legs that
just hang there. Proverbs 26:7

A fool shows everyone how stupid he is.
Ecclesiastes 10:3

A fool delights in airing his own opinions. Proverbs 18:2

A fool repeats his foolishness like a dog returns to his
vomit. Proverbs 26:11

MISH MASH

When Jeremiah wrote scrolls to be read to Jehoiakim, he dictated them to Baruch, his secretary. Jeremiah 36:4

John heard a voice like a trumpet while on the island of Patmos. Revelation 1:10

God inflicted Pharaoh with diseases for taking Abram's wife. Genesis 12:17

Amos prophesied two years before an earthquake.
Amos 1:1

The new Jerusalem will never get dark. Revelation 21:25

When Jewish exiles left Persia to build the temple in Jerusalem, they took 30 gold dishes, 1,000 silver dishes, 29 silver pans, 30 gold bowls, and 410 silver bowls.
Bon voyage. Ezra 1:9-10

> **?** Who said, "What is man that you
>   are mindful of him?"
>
> *David. Psalm 8:4*

Jashobeam, Eleazar, and Shammah were known as "the three." They were David's mightiest men.
1 Chronicles 11:11-12, 2 Samuel 23:11

A IS FOR APPLE—

or is it? Find just a few of the "A" names found in the Bible.

```
A A N D R E W O R A A
P B A H A H A Z B A D
A I A G U M Z I A R O
B S P Y S O M A T O N
I H L E M E B B H N I
G A U A L R O E A A J
A G D E A N H D L Q A
I A C H A P A N I U H
L H A H A R B E A I D
F M C S Z V E G H L A
G A A B S A L O M A T
```

Aaron	Amos	Andrew
Abednego	Abel	Aquila
Abigail	Athaliah	Abimelech
Asaph	Abraham	Adonijah
Absalom	Abishag	Achan
Ahab	Adam	Ahaz

WORDSEARCH SOLUTION

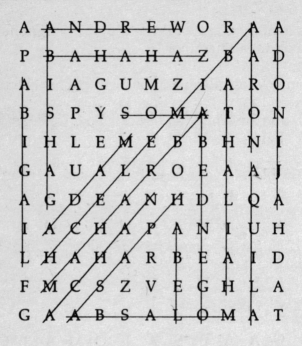

```
A A N D R E W O R A A
P B A H A H A Z B A D
A I A G U M Z I A R O
B S P Y S O M A T O N
I H L E M E B B H N I
G A U A L R O E A A J
A G D E A N H D L Q A
I A C H A P A N I U H
L H A H A R B E A I D
F M C S Z V E G H L A
G A A B S A L O M A T
```

? Who said, "Who is there that the king would rather honor than me?"

Haman, Esther 6:6

I FEEL A SONG COMIN' ON

Who composed these songs found in the Scripture?

1. "Her hand reached for the tent peg, her right hand for the workman's hammer."

2. "From now on all generations will call me blessed. . ."

3. "And you, my child, will be called a prophet of the Most High."

4. "By the blast of your nostrils the waters piled up."

5. "Keep me safe, O God, for in you I take refuge."

6. "I will sing for the one I love, a song about his vineyard. . ."

7. "The Lord brings death and makes alive; he brings down to the grave and raises up."

8. "Glory to God in the highest and on earth peace to men on whom his favor rests."

9. "The Lord is my rock, my fortress and my deliverer."

10. "Like arrows in the hands of a warrior are sons born in one's youth."

ANSWERS

1. Deborah and Barak. Judges 5:26

2. Mary. Luke 1:46

3. Zechariah. Luke 1:76

4. Moses and the Israelites. Exodus 15:8

5. David. Psalm 16:1

6. Isaiah. Isaiah 5:1

7. Hannah. 1 Samuel 2:6

8. Heavenly Hosts. Luke 2:15

9. David. 2 Samuel 22:2

10. Solomon. Psalm 127:4

Pass the Fig Leaves, Please

A list of naked people.

Noah was naked after he fell down drunk. Genesis 9:21

Adam and Eve. Genesis 2:25

Death is naked before God. Ok, it's a thing, not a person. Job 26:6

A young man who had been following Jesus ran away naked when his loin cloth fell off. Mark 14:51-52

Seven sons of Sceva were attacked by a demon-possessed man, and they ran away bleeding and naked. Acts 19:16

Isaiah was stripped and barefoot for three years. 1 Samuel 20:3

When the men of Sodom tried to capture Lot's special guests, they were all struck blind. Genesis 19:11

In the new earth and heaven there isn't a sea. Revelation 21:1

If you wink maliciously, you'll cause grief.
Proverbs 10:10

On the Sabbath day in Jerusalem, Nehemiah shut all the doors to the city so merchants couldn't violate Sabbath rules. Nehemiah 13:19

A woman named Sheerah built Lower and Upper Beth Horon. 1 Chronicles 7:24

Because Jehoraim was an evil king, God afflicted him with a disease of the bowels. Take that! 2 Chronicles 21:18

Noah only had seven days to gather up all the animals into the ark. Genesis 7:3-4

Zechariah saw a flying scroll 30 feet long and 15 feet wide. In-coming! Zechariah 5:2

The Lord whistles for those at the ends of the earth. Isaiah 5:26

GUESS WHO I AM

In this multiple choice quiz, choose the judge who fits the description.

A. Othniel B. Ehud C. Shamgar
D. Deborah E. Gideon F. Tola
G. Jair H. Jephthah I. Samson

1. He blew his trumpet and smashed his empty jar.
   E C I

2. This left-handed judge stabbed a king with a home-made sword.
   B F I

3. This one killed 600 Philistines with an ox goad.
   C E G

4. This judge was Caleb's nephew.
   A B E

5. This one said, "With a donkey's jawbone I have made donkeys of them."
   I A C

6. He had 30 sons on 30 donkeys and controlled 30 towns.
   G F H

7. This judge sacrificed his only child because of a vow he made to the Lord.
   H C B

8. When Barak was afraid to confront an enemy alone, this judge went with him.
   D B H

ANSWERS

1. E. Gideon. Judges 7:19

2. B. Ehud. Judges 3:21

3. C. Shamgar. Judges 4:8-9

4. A. Othniel. Judges 3:9

5. I. Samson. Judges 15:16

6. G. Jair. Judges 10:4

7. H. Jephthah. Judges 11:30-39

8. D. Deborah. Judges 4:8-9

WHAT'S IN A NAME?

Unscramble the common and not-so-common biblical names for God.

1. hhimsgot (2 words)

2. gdjue

3. ysniectanfoda (3 words)

4. hdorewt (2 words)

5. dgeentrnlao (2 words)

6. ndngeadhtngnebieni (4 words)

7. hhvoaje

8. jbtoniofacpor (3 words)

9. relpefhoasio (3 words)

10. fogtimjcbaohynoe (4 words)

ANSWERS

1. Most High. Genesis 14:18-20

2. Judge. Genesis 18:25

3. Ancient of Days. Daniel 7:9

4. The Word. John 1:1

5. Eternal God. Genesis 21:33

6. Beginning and the End. Revelation 1:8

7. Jehovah.

8. Portion of Jacob. Jeremiah 10:16

9. Hope of Israel. Jeremiah 14:8

10. Mighty One of Jacob. Genesis 49:24

Four!

No, you're not golfing, you're reading a list of four-things in the Bible.

The garden of Eden had four rivers. Genesis 2:10

If an Israelite stole someone's sheep, he had to pay it back with four sheep. Exodus 22:1

The ark of the covenant has four gold rings. Exodus 25:12

The lampstand had four cups shaped like almond flowers. Exodus 25:34

The Most Holy Place had a curtain hung with gold hooks on four posts that stood on four silver bases. Exodus 26:32

Jephthah's daughter spent four months with her friends before she was sacrificed. Judges 19:2

Elijah poured four jars of water on his offering when competing with followers of Baal, three times even. 1 Kings 18:33

Bathsheba and David had four children. 1 Chronicles 3:5

Ezekiel saw four living creatures each with four faces and four wings. Ezekiel 1:5-6

HONEY, A MEAN WIFE, AND OTHER THINGS

If you eat too much honey, you'll throw up. Proverbs 25:16

When Zechariah, John the Baptist's father, was mute, people seemed to think he was deaf, too. Luke 1:62

When Cain was banished from Eden, God put a mark on him so no one would kill him. Genesis 4:15

The new Jerusalem will be 1,400 miles long and 1,400 miles wide. Revelation 21:16

It's better to live on the roof than to live inside with a mean wife. Proverbs 21:9

> **?** Of the three kings who reigned during the rebuilding of the temple in Jerusalem, who was in power when it was finished—Cyrus, Darius, or Artaxerxes?
>
> *Darius. Ezra 6:15*

When Reuben slept with Jacob's concubine Bilhah, he lost his birthright to Joseph. Genesis 35:22, 1 Chronicles 5:1

Solomon's throne had six steps with twelve lions sitting on them. 2 Chronicles 9:18

I HAVE A DREAM

Who had these dreams?

1. He saw a statue whose feet were smashed by a stone.

2. Four winds of heaven stirred up the sea in this man's dream.

3. A giant tree had enough fruit for everybody.

4. They were warned in a dream about Herod's evil scheme.

5. He was warned to take his family to Egypt.

6. He saw angels going up and down on a ladder.

7. His brothers were annoyed with his dreams, one of which involved the moon and stars.

8. This ruler dreamed about some hefty cows eating some scrawny ones.

9. He saw a vine produce grapes and squeezed their juice into a cup.

10. She had an unpleasant dream and blamed it on Jesus.

ANSWERS

1. Nebuchadnezzar. Daniel 2:31-34

2. Daniel. Daniel 7:2

3. Nebuchadnezzar again. Daniel 4:10-12

4. The magi. Matthew 2:12

5. Joseph. Matthew 2:13

6. Jacob. Genesis 28:12

7. Joseph. Genesis 37:9

8. Pharaoh. Genesis 41:1-4

9. Pharoah's cup bearer. Genesis 40:9-11

10. Pilate's wife. Matthew 27:19

SOMETHING OLD...

After reading the New Testament quote, name the Old Testament passage to which it refers or even duplicates.

1. "...for out of you will come a ruler who will be the shepherd of my people Israel." Matthew 2:6

2. "You will be with child and give birth to a son, and you are to give him the name Jesus." Luke 1:31

3. "When they had crucified him, they divided up his clothes by casting lots. " Matthew 27:35

4. "But when they came to Jesus and found that he was already dead, they did not break his legs." John 19:33

5. "Jesus found a young donkey and sat upon it, as it is written, '...see, your king is coming, seated on a donkey's colt.'" John 12:14-15

6. "'What are you willing to give me if I hand him over to you?' so they counted out 30 pieces of silver." Matthew 26:15

7. "And the scripture was fulfilled which says, 'He was counted with the lawless ones.'" Mark 15:28

8. "The blind receive sight, the lame walk, and the deaf hear." Matthew 11:5

9. "A voice of one calling in the desert, 'Prepare the way of the Lord, make straight paths for him.'" Matthew 3:3

10. "But I, when I am lifted up from the earth, will draw all men to myself." John 12:32

ANSWERS

1. Micah 5:2

2. Isaiah 7:14

3. Psalm 22:18

4. Psalm 34:20

5. Zechariah 9:9

6. Zechariah 11:12

7. Isaiah 53:12

8. Isaiah 35:5-6

9. Isaiah 40:3

10. Isaiah 33:10

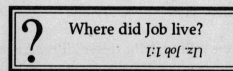

? **Where did Job live?**
Uz, Job 1:1

WOE IS ME

All these people tore their clothes as a sign of distress for one reason or another.

Joshua and Caleb tore their clothes while trying to convince the people that Canaan was really attainable. Number 14:6

Joshua tore his when the Lord allowed the Israelites to lose in battle. Joshua 7:6

Jephthah tore his clothes when he realized that he had to sacrifice his daughter. Judges 11:35

David and his men tore theirs when they mourned for Saul and David. 2 Samuel 1:11

Tamar tore her robe after Amnon raped her. 2 Samuel 13:19

Ahab tore his for fear of being eaten by dogs. 1 Kings 21:27

King Joziah tore his when he heard the Book of the Law being read. 2 Kings 22:11

Mordecai tore his clothes when Haman plotted to kill the Jews. Esther 4:1

Paul and Barnabas tore their clothes when people in Lystra thought they were gods. Acts 14:14

When Paul needed to escape from Damascus, his friends lowered him from the city wall in a basket. Acts 9:25

It's better to be with a mad bear than with a fool. Proverbs 17:12

Once, David's mightiest men risked their lives to get him some water from a well, but David wouldn't drink it because of all the trouble they went to. 1 Chronicles 11:17-19

> **?** If a cheerful heart is good medicine, what does a crushed spirit do?
>
> Dry up the bones. Proverbs 17:22

When King David conquered Ammonite towns, he forced the occupants to labor with saws, picks, and axes. 1 Chronicles 20:3

Once the people in the synagogue in Nazareth were so disgusted with Jesus that they tried to throw him off of a cliff. Luke 4:29

Golgotha means "The Place of The Skulls." Mark 15:22

Gideon was also known as Jerub-Baal. Judges 7:1

Only priests could carry the ark of the covenant. 1 Corinthians 15:2

WILL THE REAL MARY. . .

Which Mary fits the description?
  A. Mary Magdalene
  B. Mary, Jesus' Mother
  C. Mary, the wife of Clopas
  D. Mary, Martha's Sister

1. This Mary poured expensive perfume on Jesus' feet and wiped it off with her hair.

2. Seven demons were driven out of this Mary.

3. These Marys were the first people to whom Jesus appeared after his resurrection.

4. Jesus handed John the apostle over to this Mary as a son.

5. This Mary was scolded for not helping to make dinner.

6. When this Mary's brother died, Jesus came to the rescue and brought him back to life.

ANSWERS

1. D. Mary, Martha's sister. John 11:2

2. A. Mary Magdalene. Luke 8:2

3. A, C. Mary Magdalene and Mary, the wife of Clopas.
   Mark 16:9

4. B. Mary, Jesus' mother. John 19:25

5. D. Mary, Martha's sister. Luke 10:40

6. D. Mary, Martha's sister. John 11:43

TRAVELIN' MAN

Label this map
and name
what Jesus
did in each place.

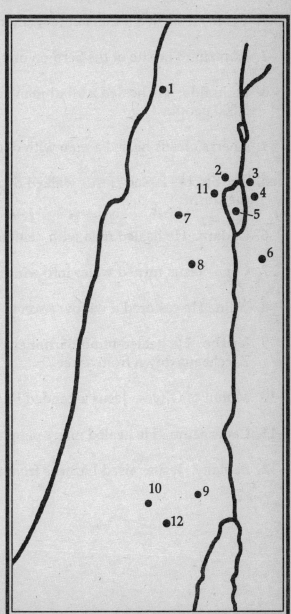

ANSWERS

1. Tyre. He healed a Canaanite woman's daugther.

2. Korazin. The site of the Sermon on the Mount.

3. Bethsaida. He healed a blind man and fed more than 5,000 people.

4. Khersa. Jesus healed a man with demons. Luke 8:26

5. The Sea of Galilee. Jesus walked on water and calmed the storm.

6. Gadara. He healed men with demons. Matthew 8:28

7. Cana. Jesus turned water into wine.

8. Nain. He restored a widow's son to life.

9. Jericho. He healed blind Bartimieus and called Zacchaeus down from a tree.

10. Mount of Olives. Jesus ascended into heaven.

11. Capernaum. He healed many people here.

12. Bethany. Jesus raised Lazarus from the dead.

FEED ME, HEAL ME

If you stay awake, you'll have extra food. Proverbs 20:13

After David brought the ark back to Jerusalem, he gave a cake of raisins and cake of dates to each Israelite. 1 Chronicles 16:3

Once Jesus healed a mute man by spitting and touching the guy's tongue. Say ah. Mark 7:33

King Amaziah had 10,000 of his enemies killed by marching them off of a cliff. 2 Chronicles 25:12

> **?** When Jesus said, "Man does not live by bread alone, but on every word that comes from the mouth of God," what verse was he quoting?
>
> *Deuteronomy 8:3 (Mark 4:4)*

People were healed just by touching Jesus' clothes. Mark 6:56

Hosanna means "save now."

DRESSED FOR SUCCESS

Jermiah wore a linen belt that couldn't get wet.
Jeremiah 13:1

In a vision, Joshua wore a clean turban to show that his sins
had been taken away. Zechariah 3:4-5

Israelite priests wore a breast piece, an ephod, a robe, a
tunic, a turban, and a sash. Exodus 28:4

Early Christian women wore head coverings when they
prayed and prophesied. 1 Corinthians 11:5

Early Christian men didn't. 1 Corinthians 11:4

Israelites wore tassels on their clothes to remind them of
God's commands. Numbers 15:37-41

OH, THOSE PROPHETS

They had so much to say. Which one said each of these gems?

1. "Dry bones, hear the word of the Lord."

2. "Beat your plowshares into swords and your pruning hooks into spears."

3. "Seaweed was wrapped around my head."

4. "The Lord is God, a refuge in times of trouble."

5. "They will beat their swords into plowshares and their spears into pruning hooks."

6. "For He (the Lord) will be like a refiner's fire or a launderer's soap."

7. "Holy, holy, holy is the Lord Almighty; the whole earth is full of his glory."

8. "The heart is deceitful above all things and beyond cure. Who can understand it."

9. "Give us nothing but vegetables to eat and water to drink."

10. "Hear this word, you cows of Bashan on Mount Samaria, you women who oppress the poor and crush the needy."

ANSWERS

1. Ezekiel. Ezekiel 37:4

2. Joel. Joel 3:10

3. Jonah. Jonah 2:5

4. Nahum. Nahum 1:7

5. Micah. Micah 4:3

6. Malachi. Malachi 3:2

7. Isaiah. Isaiah 6:3

8. Jeremiah. Jeremiah 17:9

9. Daniel. Daniel 1:12

10. Amos. Amos 4:1

CRAZY CROSSWORD

Fill in the squares with two verses from the New Testament. No, not just any verses. Here are some clues. 1. All the Ws have been given. 2. These verses are an introduction of sorts written by someone whom Jesus referred to as His beloved.

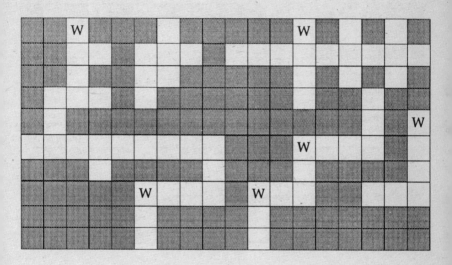

ANSWERS

The verses are John 1:1-2 and here is how they might fit into the puzzle:

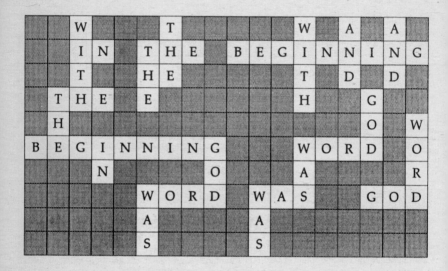

"This is the disciple who testifies to these things and who wrote them down. We know that his testimony is true. Jesus did many other things as well. If every one of them were written down, I suppose that even the whole world would not have room for the books that would be written." John 21:24-25

The last two verses of John, in case you were wondering.

Camp Rules for the Hebrew

*There are some things you just shouldn't have
to tell a person.*

Don't take advantage of orphans or widows. Exodus 22:22

Don't follow the crowd. Exodus 23:2

Every year, have three great big parties. Exodus 23:14

If you buy a Hebrew servant, you have to let him go after six years. Exodus 21:2

If a man marries more than one women, he can't deny the first wife food, clothes, and marital rights. Exodus 21:10

Don't eat animals that chew cud. Rabbits and camels, for example. Leviticus 11:4-5

Don't eat blood. Or is it drink blood? Leviticus 17:14

Don't cut yourself on purpose. Leviticus 19:28

Stand up around the elderly. Leviticus 19:32

Don't offer an animal with warts as an offering.
Leviticus 22:22

Remember the story of Uzzah who died because he touched the ark of the covenant? The event made David angry with God, so he named the place Perez-Uzzah.
1 Chronicles 13:11

Rehoboam, Solomon's son, had 28 sons and 60 daughters.
2 Chronicles 11:21

The Israelites couldn't eat storks.
Leviticus 11:19

Some people, including Herod, thought that Jesus was John the Baptist raised from the dead. Mark 6:14

Some other people, thought He was Elijah. Mark 6:15

God made Adam and Eve's first clothes, aside from the fig leaves, of course. Genesis 3:21

God allowed Israel to drive out other nations from Canaan because those nations were evil, not because Israel was so righteous. Deuteronomy 9:4-5

During the Passover, Israelites couldn't break any of the bones in their feast, not even the wishbone. Exodus 12:46

Jesus chose 72 people to travel by twos ahead of him and to heal people. Luke 10:10

WHO AM I?

1. I lived in Antioch and predicted a severe famine that affected the entire Roman world.

2. I died when Joab stabbed me in the stomach. I miss being the commander of Saul's army.

3. Because I was the god of Ekron, Ahaziah tried to consult me about a certain injury.

4. My husband Felix and I listened to Paul talk about Jesus while he was on trial.

5. After I died, my widow Naomi and our devoted daughter-in-law had to begin a new life.

6. I gave my friend David my clothes, my sword, my bow, and my belt.

7. As an archangel, I argued with the devil over Moses' body.

8. My king, David, forced me into a disastrous battle, and when I was killed he married my wife.

9. My useless husband replaced me as queen with a Jewish girl.

10. As king of Moab, I tried to hire Balaam to curse Israel.

ANSWERS

1. Agabus. Acts 11:28

2. Abner. 2 Samuel 3:27

3. Baal-Zebub. 2 Kings 1:2

4. Drusilla. Acts 24:24

5. Elimelech. Ruth 1:3

6. Jonathan. 1 Samuel 18:4

7. Michael. Jude 9

8. Uriah. 2 Samuel 11:15

9. Vashti. Esther 2:1-4

10. Balak. Numbers 22:24

WHERE'S THE VERSE?

You know it's in there somewhere, don't you.

1. "I am the resurrection and the life. He who believes in me will live even though he dies."

2. "Here I am. I stand at the door and knock."

3. "That if you confess with your mouth, 'Jesus is Lord,' and believe in your heart that God raised Him from the dead, you will be saved."

4. "For this reason a man will leave his father and mother and be united to his wife, and they will become one flesh."

5. "Our Father in heaven, hallowed be your name."

6. "A record of the genealogy of Jesus Christ the son of David, the son of Abraham:..."

7. "For as lightning that comes from the east is visible even in the west, so will be the coming of the Son of Man."

8. "It is easier for a camel to go through the eye of a needle than for a rich man to enter the kingdom of Heaven."

9. "Let him kiss me with the kisses of his mouth—for your love is more delightful than wine."

10. "Everyone must submit himself to the governing authorities, for there is no authority except that which God has established."

ANSWERS

1. John 11:25

2. Revelation 3:20

3. Romans 10:9

4. Genesis 2:24

5. Matthew 6:9

6. Matthew 1:1

7. Matthew 24:27

8. Matthew 9:23

9. Song of Songs 1:2

10. Romans 13:1

Once when Paul and Silas were in prison,
an earthquake shook the doors open.
Acts 16:26

Jesus means "the Lord saves."

When Aaron and his sons were ordained, Moses had to put ram's blood on their right ear lobes, right thumbs, and right big toes. Exodus 29:20

Priscilla and Aquila moved to Corinth because Claudius, the emperor, made all the Jews leave Rome. Acts 18:2

All the tribes of Israel got part of the promised land except the Levites. Numbers 26:62

Jesus once made some demons keep quiet after He drove them out because they knew who He was, and He wanted to keep His identity to himself for awhile. Mark 1:34

People with running sores couldn't present offerings to God. Leviticus 21:18

If an Israelite wanted to marry a captive woman, he had to make her shave her head, trim her nails, and change her clothes. So much for the lovely bride.
Deuteronomy 21:12-13

Whenever evil spirits saw Jesus, they fell down and yelled, "You are the Son of God." Mark 3:11

FOUR-THINGS

There were too many to fit on one page

Zacchaeus paid back the people he cheated four times over. Luke 19:8

Peter was arrested by four squads of four soldiers each. Acts 12:4

Philip had four prophesying daughters. Acts 21:9

John saw four creatures in front of the throne, and they were covered with eyes. Revelation 4:6

Lazarus was in his tomb for four days. John 11:37

After Jesus was crucified, the soldiers divided up His clothes into four shares. John 19:23

Zechariah saw four chariots, four craftsman, and four horses. Zechariah 1:18, 20, 6:1

Daniel saw four winds of heaven and four beasts, at least one with four wings and four heads. Daniel 7:3-6

SOLOMON'S QUANDRY

That Solomon, what a guy! Finish his thoughts from Proverbs 30 on the things that perplexed him.

1. "Four things on earth are small, yet they are extremely wise." What are they?

2. "There are three things that are never satisfied, four that never say, 'Enough.'" What are they?

3. "There are three things that are too amazing for me, four that I do not understand." What are they?

4. "Under three things the earth trembles, under four it cannot bear up." What are they?

5. "There are three things that are stately in their stride, four that move with stately bearing." What are they?

ANSWERS

1. Ants, coneys, locusts, and lizards. Verses 24-28

2. The grave, a barren womb, land that needs water, and fire. Verses 15-16

3. The eagle, the snake, a ship, and a man with a maiden. Verses 18-20

4. A servant who becomes a king, a fool full of food, an unloved woman who is married, and a maid who displaces her mistress. Verses 21-23

5. The lion, a strutting rooster, a he-goat, and a king with his army. Verses 29-31

Wisdom was made before the world began.
Proverbs 8:23

Z Is for Zebra

and that's not all! Find the biblical names that begin with Z in this wordsearch.

```
A  H  A  I  D  A  B  E  Z  Z  Z
B  Z  Y  Z  A  B  B  A  I  E  E
I  Z  O  P  H  A  R  D  P  B  R
Z  E  D  E  K  I  A  H  P  U  U
M  C  A  I  H  B  A  A  O  L  B
H  H  L  N  A  N  S  R  R  U  B
A  A  T  Z  I  O  J  E  A  N  A
P  R  N  A  V  A  A  Z  H  K  B
L  I  H  C  Z  E  B  E  D  E  E
I  A  N  T  M  A  H  T  E  Z  L
Z  H  Z  A  C  C  H  A  E  U  S
```

Zaavan   Zephaniah   Zabad
Zerubbabel   Zabbai   Zilpah
Zacchaeus   Zipporah   Zebadiah
Zerah   Zebedee   Zetham
Zebulun   Ziba   Zechariah
        Zophar   Zedekiah

WORDSEARCH SOLUTION

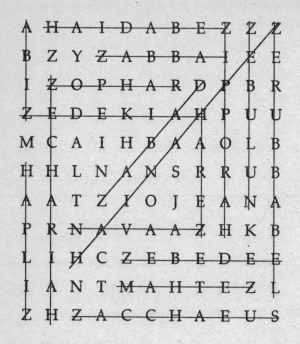

? This servant of Saul's told David that Saul was survived by a son named Mephibosheth. Who was he?

Ziba. 2 Samuel 9:4

HOOK, LINE, AND SOLDIER

Under David's rule, there were more than one million men who could handle a sword in Israel. 1 Chronicles 21:5

Solomon built the temple on Mount Moriah.
2 Chronicles 3:1

Ham, Noah's son, was the father of Canaan. Genesis 11:22

> **?** Where was Paul when he had his hair cut off?
> *Cenchrea. Acts 18:18*

When the Assyrians took Manasseh prisoner, they put a hook in his nose. 2 Chronicles 33:11

Jochebed, Moses' mother, married Amram, Moses' father, who was her nephew. Does that make Moses and Amram cousins, or what? Exodus 6:20

After Jesus was resurrected, He ate a piece of boiled fish with His disciples. Luke 24:42-43

While some priests were carrying the ark of the covenant, the Jordan River dried up so they could cross on dry ground. Joshua 3:15-17

EAT, DRINK, AND BE. . .

"Do not get drunk on wine, which leads to debauchery,"
Ephesians 5:18. Here is a list of people who either didn't heed this
timeless advice or were just misunderstood.

Noah. He was definitely not misunderstood. Genesis 9:21

Eli thought Hannah was drunk, but she was just praying quietly. 1 Samuel 1:13

On the day of Pentecost, some people thought the believers had had too much wine. Acts 2:13

Lot, more than once. Genesis 19:33, 35

Jesus was called a drunkard by some of the Pharisees. Matthew 11:19

Nabal, whose wife Abigail saved him from the wrath of David. 1 Samuel 25:36

Uriah got drunk the night before he died in battle, thanks to David. 2 Samuel 11:13

"Drink, get drunk, and vomit."
Jeremiah 25:27

IT HAPPENED IN THE NEW TESTAMENT...DIDN'T IT?

Answer the following True/False questions pertaining to the New Testament.

1. Hezekiah was John the Baptist's father.

2. Tiberius Caesar was ruler when Jesus was born.

3. Jesus made some healing mud by mixing His saliva with dirt.

4. Peter was the disciple "whom Jesus loved."

5. Paul and Barnabas had such a disagreement that they parted company.

6. It was nearly dusk when the Lord caused a bright light to blind Paul.

7. Paul survived a harrowing shipwreck in the Black Sea.

8. Stephen was seized by a disgruntled group called the Synagogue of the Freedmen.

9. Paul had a secretary named Tertius.

10. Mark and Barnabas were brothers.

ANSWERS

1. False. Zechariah was his father. Luke 1:15

2. False. Caesar Augustus was the ruler. Luke 2:1

3. True. John 9:6

4. False. John is believed to be the one. John 13:23

5. True. Acts 15:39

6. False. It was about noon. Acts 22:6

7. False. It is never recorded that he was in the Black Sea.

8. True. Acts 6:9-12

9. True. Romans. 16: 22

10. False. They were cousins. Colossians 4:10

Bless Me, Please

To which of his many sons was Jacob referring when he handed out these blessings. (Genesis 49)

1. "...is a fruitful vine whose branches climb over a wall."

2. "Cursed be their anger, so firece, and their fury, so cruel!"

3. "...will be a serpent by the roadside, a viper along the path."

4. " He will live by the seashore."

5. "...he will bend his shoulder to the burden and submit to forced labor."

6. "You are my firstborn, my might, the first sign of my strength."

7. "...will be attacked by a band of raiders."

8. "He will tether his donkey to a vine, his colt to the choicest branch."

9. "His food will be rich."

10. "He is a doe set free that bears beautiful fawns."

11. "He devours his prey in the morning and divides the plunder at night."

ANSWERS

1. Joseph.

2. Simeon and Levi.

3. Dan.

4. Zebulun.

5. Issachar.

6. Reuben.

7. Gad.

8. Judah.

9. Asher.

10. Naphtali.

11. Benjamin.

Ah, Man's Best Friend

Dogs didn't bark at the Israelites during the plague on the firstborn in Egypt. Exodus 11:7

Dogs ate those belonging to Jeroboam. 1 Kings 14:11

Dogs ate those belonging to Baasha. 1 Kings 16:4

And, dogs ate those belonging to Ahab. 1 Kings 21:24

In fact, dogs licked up Ahab's blood. 1 Kings 22:38

Dogs ate Jezebel, except for her hands and feet.
2 Kings 9:33-36

"Anyone who is among the living has hope—even
a live dog is better off than a dead lion!"
Ecclesiastes 9:4

When Philip met the Ethiopian eunuch, the eunuch was reading Isaiah 53:7-8. Acts 8:32-33

God didn't allow David to build a house for Him because he had caused too much death. Solomon got to do it instead. 1 Chronicles 22:8-10

Once when Peter was really hungry, he saw a sheet full of animals in a vision, and God told him to eat up. Acts 10:10-13

When Uzziah, an unfaithful king, tried to burn incense to the Lord, leprosy broke out on his forehead. 2 Chronicles 26:19

? Who said, "Why do you spend the night by the wall? If you do this again, I will lay hands on you."

Nehemiah. Nehemiah 13:20

If the disciples had paid for the food to feed the 5,000-plus people, it would have cost eight months' pay. Mark 6:37

Jericho is the "city of palms." 2 Chronicles 28:15

Remember the stone Jacob used as a pillow the night he dreamed about angels? He used the same stone as a pillar to mark the spot. Genesis 28:18

LIKE, A VALLEY QUIZ, YA KNOW

1. The Lord will bring judgment in the Valley of _____.

2. The Valley of Ben Hinnom will become known as the Valley of _____.

3. David killed 18,000 Edomites in the Valley of _____.

4. When people of Sodom and Gomorrah ran from enemy kings, they got stuck in tar pits in the Valley of _____.

5. The 12 spies of Israel got a huge cluster of grapes from the Valley of _____.

6. Achan was stoned and his body was covered with rocks in the Valley of _____.

7. It was in the Valley of _____ that Gideon tested the Lord with a fleece.

8. In the _____ Valley, King Asa burned his grandmother's asherah pole.

9. "Even though I walk through the valley of the _____ _____ _____, I will fear no evil."

ANSWERS

1. Jehoshophat. Joel 3:12

2. Slaughter. Jeremiah 7:32

3. Salt. 2 Samuel 8:13

4. Siddim. Genesis 14:3

5. Eshcol. Numbers 13:23

6. Achor. Joshua 7:26

7. Jezreel. Judges 6:33-40

8. Kidron. 2 Chronicles 15:16

9. Shadow of death. Psalm 23:4

HE WHO HAS EARS
LET HIM HEAR

To whom was Jesus speaking when He said. . .

1. "It is written: 'Man does not live on bread alone, but on every word that comes from the mouth of God.'"

2. "Go! It will be done just as you believed it would."

3. "It is not right to make the children's bread and toss it to their dogs."

4. "Quiet! Be still!"

5. "Get behind me, Satan! You do not have in mind the things of God, but the things of men."

6. "You don't know what you are asking. Can you drink the cup I drink or be baptized with the baptism I am baptized with?"

7. "Go, show yourselves to the priests."

8. "Dear woman, why do you involve me? My time has not yet come"

9. "Go, call your husband and come back."

10. "Your brother will rise again."

ANSWERS

1. Satan. Matthew 4:4

2. The centurion. Matthew 8:13

3. A Canaanite woman. Matthew 15:26

4. The wind and the waves. Mark 4:39

5. Peter. Mark 8:33

6. James and John. Mark 10:38

7. The ten healed lepers. Luke 17:14

8. Mary. John 2:4

9. The Samaritan woman who actually had five husbands.
   John 4:16

10. Martha. John 11:23

PLENTIFUL POT POURRI

Once, so many people crammed into a house with Jesus that He and His disciples couldn't even eat. Mark 3:20

When the Lord killed the firstborn of Egypt, he even killed the firstborn animals. Exodus 13:15

? Who owned the cattle on 1,000 hills?

Asaph. Psalm 50:10

In order to feed the large crowd of more than 5,000, Jesus organized the people into groups of 100s and 50s.
Mark 6:39-40

While Abimelech governed Israel, he murdered his 70 brothers. Judges 9:5

On the day of Pentecost, a violent wind filled the house where the believers had gathered. Acts 2:2

A woman cracked Abimelech's head with a stone, so he told his armor-bearer to kill him. He didn't want people to say, "a woman killed him." Judges 9:53-54

People used to lay sick people in the streets so that Peter's shadow could heal them as he walked by. Acts 5:15

DEFINITIVE DEFINITIONS

An ephod is a sleeveless vest worn by priests.

Abba means "dear father" in Aramaic.

Ben, as in Ben-Hadad, means "son" in Hebrew.

Messiah means "anointed one" in Hebrew.

A bier was a bed used for corpses. See 2 Samuel 3:31

Henna, like the blossoms in Song of Songs, is a bush with leaves that are used to color fingernails.

Gall is a bitter extract from a plant in Palestine.

Offal is the waste part of an animal that was burned as an offering.

OLD TESTAMENT TRUE FALSE

1. When the Israelites left Egypt, they numbered more than 600,000 men, plus women and children.

2. The Passover feast commemorates the day the Israelites were released from Babylon.

3. Tola and Jair were ungodly kings who were defeated by the Midianites as a judgment from God.

4. Samson was from the tribe of Dan.

5. Walleye was the father of Boaz.

6. Gehazi was the name of Elisha's servant.

7. King Zedekiah was the grandson of Jeremiah the prophet.

8. In the last chapter of the Old Testament, Micah wrote about the day of the Lord and the coming of Elijah.

9. Moses killed an Egyptian once and buried his body in the sand.

10. Israelites had trouble conquering Ai because of Achan's sin.

ANSWERS

1. True. Exodus 12:38

2. False. It commemorated their release from Egypt.
    Exodus 12

3. False. They were judges. Judges 10:1-5

4. True. Judges 13:2

5. False. Salmon was his father. Ruth 4:21

6. True. 2 Kings 4:12

7. False. Jeremiah was his grandfather, but not Jeremiah
    the prophet. Jeremiah 52:1

8. False. It was Malachi.

9. True. Exodus 2:12-13

10. True. Joshua 7

WHO SAID. . .

1. "My body is clothed with worms and scabs, my skin is broken and festering."

2. "Ah, the smell of my son is like the smell of a field that the Lord has blessed."

3. "Bless me—me too, my father!"

4. "I'm disgusted with living because of these Hittite women."

5. "You have made a fool of me! If I had a sword in my hand, I would kill you right now."

6. "If there is dew only on the fleece and all the ground is dry, then I will know that you will save Israel by my hand."

7. "What is your servant, that you should notice a dead dog like me?"

8. "This child is destined to cause the falling and rising of many in Israel, and to be a sign that will be spoken against,. . ."

9. "You brood of vipers! Who warned you to flee from the coming wrath?"

10. "I am ready not only to be bound, but also to die in Jerusalem for the name of the Lord Jesus."

ANSWERS

1. Job. Job 7:5

2. Isaac to Jacob. Genesis 27:27

3. Esau to Jacob. Genesis 27:34

4. Rebekah. Genesis 27:46

5. Balaam. Numbers 22:29

6. Gideon. Judges 6:37

7. Mephibosheth. 2 Samuel 9:8

8. Simeon while blessing the baby Jesus. Luke 2:34

9. John the Baptist. Luke 3:7

10. Paul. Acts 21:13

HANG 'EM HIGH

Haman was hanged for plotting against the Jews.
Esther 7:10

Haman's ten sons were hanged on the same gallows.
Esther 9:19

According to Matthew, Judas hanged himself after
betraying Jesus. Matthew 27:5

Bigthan and Teresh were hanged for plotting against King
Xerxes. Esther 2:23

Absalom was hanged in an oak tree by accident, although
the hanging wasn't actually the cause of his death.
2 Samuel 18:9

Pharoah hanged his chief baker, just like the guy's dream
had warned. Genesis 40:22

Ahithophel, David's counselor, hanged himself after his
plot against David was foiled. 2 Samuel 17:23

You've Got to Hear This

Esther sent clean clothes to Mordecai to replace his sack-cloth ensemble, but he wouldn't wear them. Esther 4:4

God doesn't tempt people. James 1:13

When Hezekiah and his people were purifying the temple and consecrating the priests, they sacrificed 600 bulls and 3,000 sheep and goats. 2 Chronicles 29:33

In New Testament times, when it was time for a priest to burn incense in the temple, that priest was chosen by casting lots. Luke 1:9

? Who killed Jonathan, Saul's son?

the Philistines. 1 Chronicles 10:2

King Manasseh of Judah was so rotten, he sacrificed his own sons in a fire. 2 Chronicles 33:6

Abram's name was changed to Abraham because Abraham means "father of man," and, well, Abram doesn't. Genesis 17:5

During the first Passover, the Lord killed even the first born of the livestock in Egypt. Exodus 12:29

SILVER & GOLD

and other shiny things

Choose a precious metal or stone to answer these valuable clues.

1. Abimelech paid a 1,000 shekels of this to vindicate Sarah.

2. Some of the Israelites saw the Lord standing on pavement of this.

3. The magi gave Jesus incense, myrrh, and this for a belated birthday gift.

4. Judas took 30 pieces of this to betray Jesus.

5. During a famine, a donkey's head sold for 80 shekels of this.

6. The good Samaritan gave two coins of this to the innkeeper to help the abused man.

7. There is some of this in Havilah.

8. The Proverbs 31 woman is worth more than this.

9. The 12 gates of heaven are each made a solid one of these.

10. King Nebuchadnezzar made an image of this that was 90 feet high.

ANSWERS

1. Silver. Genesis 20:16

2. Sapphire. Exodus 24:10

3. Gold. Matthew 2:11

4. Silver. Matthew 26:15

5. Silver. 2 Kings 6:25

6. Silver. Luke 10:35

7. Gold. Genesis 2:11

8. Rubies. Proverbs 31:10

9. Pearl. Revelation 21:21

10. Gold. Daniel 3:1

"Be strong and courageous" is written ten times
in the Bible. Take heed.
Deuteronomy 31:3, 6, 7; Joshua 1: 6, 7, 9, 10:25;
1 Chronicles 22:13, 28:20; 2 Chronicles 32:7

AND GOD SAID. . .

To whom was God speaking when He said. . .

1. "Ask for what ever you want me to give you.

2. "Why are you angry? Why is your face downcast?"

3. "Lift up your eyes from where you are and look north and south, east and west."

4. "Reach out your hand and take it by the tail."

5. "Stand up! What are you doing down on your face?"

6. "Rise and anoint him; he is the one."

7. "Very well, then, he is in your hands; but you must spare his life."

8. "Go and buy a linen belt and put it around your waist."

9. "Look, I am setting a plumbline among my people Israel."

10. "Do you have a right to be angry about the vine?"

ANSWERS

1. Solomon. 1 Kings 3:5

2. Cain. Genesis 4:6

3. Abram. Genesis 13:14

4. Moses. Exodus 4:4

5. Joshua. Joshua 7:10

6. Samuel. 1 Samuel 16:12

7. Satan. Job 2:6

8. Jeremiah. Jeremiah 13:1

9. Amos. Amos 7:8

10. Jonah. Jonah 4:9

Wisdom is more valuable than rubies.
Proverbs 8:11

King Josiah purged Judah by burning the priests' bones on their altars. 2 Chronicles 34:5

When Terah and his family left Ur, they were headed for Canaan but settled in Haran instead. Genesis 11:31

Jesus once cursed a fig tree so it wouldn't produce any more figs. Matthew 21:19

===

After Jacob wrestled with a "man" all night long, his name was changed to Israel. Genesis 32:28

===

Some people spread a rumor that John the apostle would never die, but it was all a misunderstanding. John 21:23

When Jericho collapsed, the Israelites killed even the animals that were inside the city. Joshua 6:21

When the Egyptians were chasing Moses and the Israelites, God made the wheels fall off of the Egyptians' chariots. Exodus 14:25

Caleb promised his daughter in marriage to the man who conquered an enemy city. His nephew won the prize. Joshua 15:16-17

Adoni-Bezek, a Canaanite, cut off the thumbs and big toes of 70 kings. Judges 1:7

20

During the flood, water covered the mountains by more than 20 feet. Genesis 7:20

The tabernacle was made with 20 frames on the south side, 20 frames on the north side, 20 posts, 20 bronze bases, and a curtain that was 20 cubits long. Exodus 26:18-27:16

Twenty was the minimum age for serving in the Israelite army. Numbers 1:3

Jacob lived with, and literally worked for, Laban's family for 20 years. Genesis 31:41

Joseph's brothers sold him for 20 shekels of silver. Genesis 37:28

King Jabin of Canaan oppressed the Israelites for 20 years while Deborah was the judge. Judges 4:3

When Moses took a census of the Israelites, everybody 20 years old or older had to pay a ransom for his life. Exodus 30:14

Samson judged Israel for 20 years. Judges 15:20

LOVE ME TENDER

Another Wordsearch

Find the dos and don'ts for love found in 1 Corinthians 13:4-8. When you're finished, gather all the remaining letters, except the Xs, unscramble them, and discover the best part of love.

```
S X E P R O T E C T S
E K N N E S A E V E N
L I V E A N H V C R O
F N Y O G T F O X S R
S D B R U E I L X T E
E U Y R V J A O X S C
E O T O E L I V E U O
K R L R U D E E I R R
I P L P A T I E N T D
N L O V E S H O P E S
G P R E S E R V E S X
```

Patient	Kind	Rejoices	Truth
Protects	Trusts	Hopes	Preserves
Envy	Boast	Proud	Rude
Self-seeking	Angry	No records	Evil
	Love (4 times)		

WORDSEARCH SOLUTION

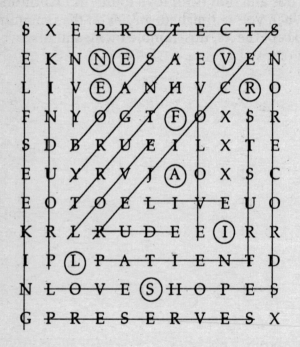

The best part of love;

Love Never Fails

MOUNTAINS

1. Noah's ark rested in the mountains of _____.

2. While Moses was tending his flock near _____, the mountain of God, he saw the burning bush.

3. Moses climbed Mount _____ in Moab and died.

4. Saul and his sons died during a fierce battle on Mount _____.

5. Solomon built a grand temple in Jerusalem on Mount _____.

6. After the Lord had an instructional supper with His disciples, they sang a hymn and went to the Mount of _____.

7. While on Mount _____, Moses took Aaron's priestly garments and gave them to Eleazar.

8. Elijah taunted 450 prophets of Ball during a contest on Mount _____.

9. In the psalm of the Sons of Korah (Psalm 48), Mount _____ is praised as the beautiful city of the Great King.

ANSWERS

1. Ararat. Genesis 8:4

2. Horeb. Exodus 3:1-2

3. Nebo. Exodus 31:1-5

4. Gilboa. 1 Samuel 31:1

5. Moriah. 2 Chronicles 3:1

6. Olives. Matthew 26:30

7. Hor. Numbers 20:27

8. Carmel. 1 Kings 18:27

9. Zion. Psalm 48:2

King Josiah provided from his own livestock 30,000 sheep and goats and 3,000 cows just for one Passover celebration. Eat up! 2 Chronicles 35:7

The Egyptians made slaves out of the Israelites because they were afraid of them. Exodus 1:9-11

Abraham's servant gave Rebekah a nose ring and two bracelets before he asked her family if she could marry Isaac. Boy, what did she get for her birthday? Genesis 24:22

When Jesus walked on the water, His disciples thought he was a ghost. Mark 6:49

> **?** The tree of the knowledge of good and evil was the downfall of Adam and Eve, as we well know. What was the name of the other symbolic tree in Eden?
>
> *The Tree of Life Genesis 2:9*

Egyptians hated shepherds. Genesis 46:34

Because the priestly garments were so sacred, Hebrew priests had to take a bath before they put them on. Leviticus 16:4

When the early Christians received the Holy Spirit, they were suddenly able to speak in foreign languages. Acts 2:4

WASH THOSE FILTHY HANDS!

The Pharisees criticized the disciples for eating with dirty hands. Mark 7:5

When the men of Judah were taking over Bethel, they spared a man who showed them how to get into the city. Judges 1:24-25

Andrew was a disciple of John the Baptist before he decided to follow Jesus. Wise choice. John 1:35-40

The Mediterranean Sea is also known as the Sea of the Philistines. Exodus 23:31

The Last Supper was a Passover feast. Mark 14:16

Deborah, the judge and prophetess, was married to a man named Lappidoth. Judges 4:4

Moses once sprinkled blood on the Israelites. Exodus 24:8

Joshua and his army won in battle against 31 enemy kings. What a fight! Joshua 12:7-24

Jesus was arrested in an olive grove of all places. John 18:1-3

MYSTERY MAN

Fill in the blanks with a name of a Bible character, unscramble the first letter of each name, and discover who wasn't circumcised until he was 99 years old.

1. _____was the eunuch assigned to Esther.

2. _____ was one of David's sisters.

3. Aaron's son, _____, was killed for offering unacceptable fire.

4. _____ was one of David's other sisters.

5. This false prophet, _____, was made blind by Paul.

6. Isaac's wife, _____, the one he really wanted, died in childbirth.

7. _____ was the son of Lot's oldest daughter, fathered by lot, incidentally.

ANSWERS

1. *H*athach. Esther 4:5

2. *A*bigail, or Abishai. 1 Chronicles 2:16-17

3. *A*bihu. Leviticus 10

4. *A*bishai, or Abigail. 1 Samuel 26:6

5. *B*ar-Jesus. Acts 13:5-12

6. *R*achel. Genesis 35:18

7. *M*oab. Genesis 19:37

The Mystery Man

Abraham. Genesis 17:24

OH, THE ANIMAL IN YOU

Many people in the Bible were compared to animals. Match these people with their respective beasts or beast parts.

People	*Animals*
1. Judah	A. Feet of a Deer
2. Issachar	B. Maggot
3. Benjamin	C. Young Stag
4. David	D. Lion's Cub
5. Ishmael	E. Dead Dog
6. The disciples	F. Rawboned Donkey
7. Man	G. Cattle
8. Mephibosheth	H. Ravenous Wolf
9. Job's friends	I. Wild Donkey
10. Solomon	J. Sheep among Wolves

ANSWERS

1. D. Lion's Cub. Genesis 49:9

2. F. Rawboned Donkey. Genesis 49:14

3. H. Ravenous Wolf. Genesis 49:27

4. A. Feet of a Deer. Psalm 18:23

5. I. Wild Donkey. Genesis 16:12

6. J. Sheep among Wolves. Matthew 10:6

7. B. Maggot. Job 25:6

8. E. Dead Dog. 2 Samuel 9:8

9. G. Cattle. Job 18:3

10. C. Young Stag. Song of Songs 2:9

PLANT ONE RIGHT HERE

*Here are just a few of the many useful plants
used in the Bible.*

Noah's dove brought an olive leaf back to the ark.
Genesis 8:11

The Israelites used hyssop to smear blood around their
door frames. Exodus 12:22

The temple lampstand was adorned with almond flowers.
Exodus 37:20

Hezekiah's boil was healed by a poultice of figs.
2 Kings 20:7

The Israelites gave a sheaf of the grain they harvested from
their new land as an offering. Leviticus 23:10

Deborah held court in the shade of a palm tree. Judges 4:5

The angel of the Lord spoke to Gideon while sitting under
an oak tree. Judges 6:11

The ostrich lays eggs in the sand and walks away because God didn't give it wisdom. He gave it speed instead. Job 39:13-18

"Is the Lord's arm too short?" That's what God said when Moses doubted His ability to feed the grumbling Hebrews. Numbers 11:22

Jerusalem has a Fish Gate. Nehemiah 3:3

In John's vision, he saw locusts who were told to torture people for five months but not to bother the grass or plants. Revelation 9:2

The Israelites celebrated the harvest for seven days, and during those days they had to live in booths. Leviticus 23:41-43

After Jesus had spent 40 days in the desert being teased by the devil, angels came down and took care of Him. Matthew 4:11

When Mary looked into Jesus' empty tomb, she saw two angels dressed in white and sitting where Jesus had been. John 20:12

It seems that God keeps hail stored up for times of trouble. Heads up! Job 38:22-23

PAUL, A COMPLICATED FELLOW

1. Why did Paul leave Titus in Crete?

2. To whom did he write a letter on behalf of Onesimus?

3. Paul was encouraged when a church remembered him fondly. What church was it?

4. Paul wrote the books of Thessalonians, but what two men were included in his opening lines?

5. Who was the metal worker who caused harm to him?

6. Besides a church organizer, prisoner, and prolific letter writer, what was Paul's other vocation?

7. What was his secret for being content?

8. Complete one of Paul's most well-known commands: "Speak to one another in _____, _____, and _____ _____."

9. Paul once addressed a church by saying "You foolish _____!" Fill in the blank.

10. To what church did Paul give "milk, not solid food."

ANSWERS

1. So he could clean up and appoint elders. Titus 1:5

2. Philemon. Philemon 1

3. The one in Thessalonica. 1 Thessalonians 3:6-7

4. Silas and Timothy.

5. Alexander. 2 Timothy 4:14

6. Tentmaker. Acts 18:3

7. "I can do everything through him who gives me strength." Philippians 4:12-13

8. Psalms, hymns, and spiritual songs. Ephesians 5:19

9. Galations. Galations 3:1

10. The Corinthians. 1 Corinthians 3:2

THE NEW MATH

*"For this very reason, make every effort to
add to your faith. . ."*

According to 2 Peter 1:5-7, what should you add to each of
the following:

1. Faith

2. Perseverance

3. Knowledge

4. Goodness

5. Brotherly kindness

6. Godliness

7. Self-control

PART 2

Fill in the blanks:

"For if you possess these _____ in increasing _____,
they will keep you from being _____ and _____ in your
_____ of our Lord Jesus Christ." 2 Peter 1:8

ANSWERS

1. To faith add goodness

2. To perseverance add godliness

3. To knowledge add self-control

4. To goodness add knowledge

5. The brotherly kindness add love

6. To godliness add brotherly kindness

7. To self-control add perseverance

PART 2

qualities, measure, ineffective,
unproductive, knowledge.

The Thessalonians weren't as noble as the Bereans.
Acts 17:11

God warned Laban in a dream not to say anything to
Laban, good or bad. Genesis 31:24

When the water in Egypt turned into blood, the smell was
so bad nobody could drink it. The smell was the least of
their problems. Exodus 7:31

When Paul was visiting the church in Galatia, he got sick
and had to be taken care of. Galations 4:14

> ? King Ahab said, "There is still one man through
> whom we can inquire of the Lord, but I hate him
> because he never prophesies anything good
> about me." About whom was he speaking?
>
> Micaiah. 1 Kings 22:8

Once, Abimelech told a story about an olive tree, fig tree,
and a vine who asked a thorn bush to be their king. It said
"yes." Judges 9:8-15

Just like dead flies make perfume stink, so does a little folly
outweigh wisdom and honor, so behave. Ecclesiastes 10:1

Paul wrote with large letters, sometimes. Galatians 6:11

50

The tabernacle curtain had 50 loops and 50 gold clasps.
Exodus 26:5-6

Absalom had 50 men running ahead of his chariot.
2 Samuel 15:1

When Obadiah hid prophets from Jezebel, he split them up
into two groups of 50. 1 Kings 18:4

David once paid 50 shekels of silver for a threshing floor
and oxen so he could make an offering that would stop a
plague. 2 Samuel 24:21-24

The gold nails in the tabernacle weighed 50 shekels.
2 Chronicles 3:9

Because of Elijah's prayer, God sent fire that killed a cap-
tain and 50 men, twice. Well, they didn't actually die
twice—there were two groups of 50 men each.
2 Kings 1:11-12

Fifty shekels of silver was the price for dedicating a male
between 20 and 60 years of age in ancient Hebrew times.
Leviticus 27:3

By Faith. . .

From the eloquent chapter of the book of Hebrews—who did these things by faith?

1. He offered God a better sacrifice than Cain.

2. He obeyed and made his home in the promised land.

3. He gave instructions about his bones.

4. He did not experience death.

5. She welcomed spies and was not killed with her disobedient neighbors.

6. He regarded disgrace for the sake of God to be greater than Egypt's treasures.

7. He condemned the world and became heir of righteousness.

8. He blessed his grandchildren while on his death bed.

9. He blessed his two children in an untraditional order.

10. His parents hid their baby because they saw that he wasn't an ordinary kid.

ANSWERS

1. Abel

2. Abraham

3. Joseph

4. Enoch

5. Rahab

6. Moses

7. Noah

8. Jacob

9. Isaac

10. Moses (Amram and Jochebed)

HOW THE TIME FLIES

"There is a time for everything, and a season for every activity under heaven." Ecclesiastes 3:1

Make a list of all the activities for which there is a time in Ecclesiastes 3:2-8 and fit them into this puzzle. Hint: The vowels have been left in for your convenience.

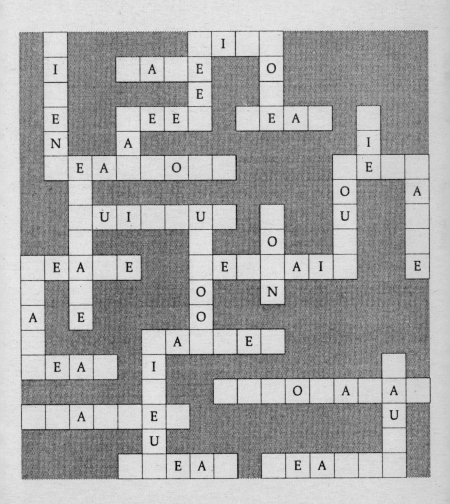

PUZZLE SOLUTION

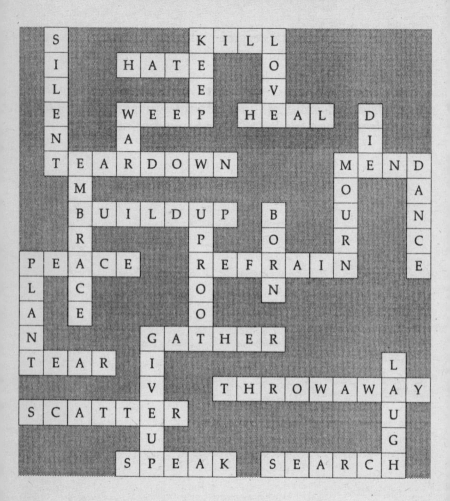

Manna was the "bread of angels." Psalm 78:25

When Jesus returns, His angels will blow trumpets to get everybody together. Matthew 24:31

There was a disabled man who sat at a gate called Beautiful everyday to beg for money, until Peter healed him.
Acts 3:2-7

A fool doesn't know how to get to town. Ecclesiastes 10:15

Even before Jacob and Esau were born, God told Rebekah that the older one would serve the younger one.
Genesis 25:23

After Jesus ascended into heaven, two men in white reassured the disciples that Jesus would come back. Who were those men in white? Acts 1:10-11

The law was given 430 years after God's covenant with Abraham was announced. Galatians 3:16-17

The author of Hebrews thought he had actually written a short letter. Imagine. Hebrews 13:22

When some angels decided to abandon the positions God had assigned to them, God bound them in chains until judgment day. Jude 6

100

Abraham was 100 when Isaac was born. Genesis 21:5

In order to marry Michal, David had to give Saul, her father, 100 Philistine foreskins. 1 Samuel 18:25

In the parable of the seeds, the seed that fell on good soil yielded crops 100 times what was sown. Luke 8:8

The hailstones that fell in John's revealing vision weighed about 100 pounds each. Revelation 16:21

Jacob once bought a camp site for 100 pieces of silver, and it didn't even have hookups. Genesis 33:19

If an Israelite man gave an Israelite woman a bad name, he was fined 100 shekels of silver, and the money went to the girl's father. Deuteronomy 22:19

Elisha once fed 100 men with only 20 loaves of barley bread, and he still had some left over. 2 Kings 4:42-44

A simple rebuke is as effective on a smart person as 100 lashes is on a fool. Proverbs 17:10

TELL ME A STORY

Here is a favorite story of many from Luke 2. Enjoy this little version, and fill in the blanks.

When Caesar _____ was ruler of the _____ world, he issued a _____ that a _____ should be taken.

So, _____ and Mary got on their donkey and traveled to _____ to be counted. Because they couldn't make _____ in those days, all of the inns were _____.

While they were staying in a barn, Mary had a _____. She wrapped him in _____ _____ and put him in a _____.

Meanwhile, some _____ were hanging around the _____ at _____, watching their _____. All of a sudden, an _____ showed up and told them some _____ news—"Today in the town of _____ a _____ has been born to you; he is _____."

Before long, a whole bunch of _____ started singing, "_____ to God in the _____, and on earth _____ to _____ on whom his _____ rests."

After the _____ caught their breath, they went to _____ to see the Christ. When they saw him, they _____ the word about the _____ in the _____.

So, after a hard day, _____ treasured everything in her _____, and the _____ went home _____ God.

The _____

ANSWERS

Paragraph 1: Augustus, Roman, decree, census

Paragraph 2: Joseph, Bethlehem, reservations, full

Paragraph 3: baby, swaddling clothes, manger

Paragraph 4: shepherds, field, night, sheep, angel, good, David, Savior, Christ

Paragraph 5: angels, Glory, highest, peace, men, favor

Paragraph 6: shepherds, Bethlehem, spread, baby, manger

Paragraph 7: Mary, heart, shepherds, praising

Paragraph 8: End

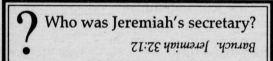

? Who was Jeremiah's secretary?

Baruch. Jeremiah 32:12

WHO KILLED WHO?

1. Abel.

2. The first born of Egypt.

3. Saul.

4. The man of God who spoke with King Jeroboam and was later found dead next to his donkey.

5. Zechariah.

6. An Egyptian who was buried in the sand.

7. Samson.

8. Goliath.

9. Abner, Saul's army commander.

ANSWERS

1. Cain. Genesis 4:8

2. God. Exodus 13:15

3. An Amalekite, because Saul asked him to.
   2 Samuel 1:8; or Saul himself. 1 Samuel 31:4

4. A lion. 1 Kings 13:24

5. The people of Judah by order of Joash.
   2 Chronicles 24:20-22

6. Moses. Exodus 2:12

7. Samson. Judges 16:30

8. David, of course. 1 Samuel 17:50

9. Joab and Abishai. 2 Samuel 3:3

? All hard work brings a profit, but what does all talk bring?

Poverty. Proverbs 14:23

Pharaoh gave Joseph an Egyptian name—Zaphenath-Paneah. Genesis 41:45

When Mary Magdalene heard someone talk to her at Jesus' tomb, she thought it was the gardner, but it was Jesus instead. John 20:15

A plague once spread through the Israelite camp that killed 24,000 people. Numbers 25:9

> **?** What do diligent hands bring?
>
> Wealth. Proverbs 10:4

In ancient times, Egyptians wouldn't eat with Hebrews. Genesis 43:32

Noah was the name of one of Zelophehad's daughters, a descendent of Manasseh. Numbers 27:1

Paul's letters were often passed around from church to church. Colossians 4:16

When the Gibeonites were retreating, God threw big hail-stones at them and killed more than the Israelites did in battle. Joshua 10:1

LET MY PEOPLE GO, OR ELSE!

Little known facts about the plagues on Egypt

After the frogs that plagued Egypt died, they were put in big piles and made a real stink. Exodus 8:32

The pestering gnats were made from all the dust in Egypt. Exodus 8:17

Moses and Aaron had to take a three-day journey to make a sacrifice to get rid of all the flies. Exodus 8:32

Egyptian magicians turned water into blood, too, so Pharaoh was not impressed with Aaron's "trick." Exodus 7:22

When the Egyptian livestock died, the Israelite animals stayed well. Exodus 9:7

Moses and Aaron gave the Egyptians boils by throwing furnace dust into the air. Exodus 9:10

Before the great hail storm, Moses gave the Egyptians enough time to get their slaves and livestock out of the fields. Exodus 9:19

When God sent darkness, no one could see anyone else for three days. Exodus 10:23

Before Pharaoh let the Israelites go after the last plague, he asked Moses and Aaron to bless him. Exodus 12:32

110

DYNAMIC DUOS

Who are the familiar, or not so familiar, duos that fit these descriptions?

1. They opposed Moses but their names are not mentioned in the Old Testament.

2. They straightened Paul out on a few things after hearing him speak in the synagogue.

3. These two prayed and sang under adverse circumstances.

4. Paul handed these people over to Satan.

5. The disagreement between these women was worthy of Paul's attention.

6. When everyone else bit their nails and knocked their knees, these two spies kept their courage.

7. These sisters had different priorities when it came to hosting Jesus.

8. These distasteful people proved to be the end of John the Baptist.

9. One was a Tishbite, and the other one was the son of Shaphat.

10. These young fighting men were "one in spirit," and they became friends, despite an antagonistic king.

ANSWERS

1. Jannes and Jambres. 2 Timothy 3:8

2. Priscilla and Aquila. Acts 18:26

3. Paul and Silas. Acts 16:25

4. Himenaeus and Alexander. 1 Timothy 1:20

5. Euodia and Syntche. Philippians 4:23

6. Joshua and Caleb. Numbers 14:6-9

7. Mary and Martha. Luke 10:39-42

8. Herod and Herodius. Matthew 14:6-10

9. Elijah and Elishah. 1 Kings 19:19

10. David and Jonathan. 1 Samuel 18:1

Sing a Little Song

Where can you find these verses that have been turned into hymns or choruses? Where in the Bible, that is?

1. "For you know that it was not with perishable things such as silver or gold that you were redeemed..."

2. "Not by might nor by power, but by my spirit."

3. "Why do the nations conspire and the peoples plot in vain?"

4. "The Lord is my light and my salvation—whom shall I fear?"

5. "This is the day the Lord has made; let us rejoice and be glad in it."

6. "Do you bring in a lamp to put it under a bowl or a bed?"

7. "See, the Lord is coming with thousands upon thousands of his holy ones..."

8. "Now to the King eternal, immortal, invisible, the only God, be honor and glory for ever and ever."

ANSWERS

1. 1 Peter 1:18

2. Zechariah 4:6

3. Psalm 2:1

4. Psalm 27:1

5. Psalm 118:24

6. Mark 4:21

7. Jude 14

8. 1 Timothy 1:17

? Paul planted the seed, Apollos watered it, but who made it grow?

God. 1 Corinthians 3:6

Kings went to war in the spring. 2 Samuel 11:1

Children have angels in heaven who always have an audi-
ence with God, so pick on someone your own size.
Matthew 18:10

While David was hiding from Saul, a priest gave him
Goliath's sword that had been saved for some reason. It
came in handy because David left his at home.
1 Samuel 21:9

Paul was from the tribe of Benjamin. Romans 11:1

> **?** Who said, "I see people; they look
> like trees walking around."
> *A blind man who Jesus healed. Mark 8:24*

The early church had a list of needy widows, but you had
to be over 60, a faithful wife (when you were a wife), and
known for good deeds. 1 Timothy 5:9

It was God who hardened Pharaoh's heart so that generation after generation of Israelites would really know that
He was the Lord. Exodus 10:1

The saints get to judge the angels. 1 Corinthians 6:3

EVERYONE KNOWS IT'S WINDY

*"The wind blows to the south and turns to the north;
round and round it goes." Ecclesiastes 1:6*

It was an east wind that brought the locusts to Egypt.
Exodus 10:13

It was a west wind that took them away. Exodus 10:19

God used an east wind to dry up part of the Red Sea.
Exodus 14:21

Isaiah prophesied that God would dry up the Egyptian sea
with a scorching wind. 1 Samuel 11:15

Wind brought quail to the dissatisfied Hebrew people.
Numbers 11:31

A strong wind knocked down Job's house, killing everybody inside. Job 1:19

On one of Paul's trips, the ship he was on was caught in a
"northeaster" for 14 days. Acts 27:14-27

God tormented Jonah with a scorching east wind. Jonah 4:8

Ark, Ark, Who's Got the Ark

1. Who made the ark of the covenant?

2. What tribe did God choose to carry it?

3. What body of water parted when the priests carried the ark into it?

4. After the Hebrews brought the ark from Shiloh, who stole it from them?

5. To whose temple did the enemies take the ark?

6. To what town did the enemies return the ark, along with a guilt offering?

7. In whose house did the Hebrews keep the ark for 20 years?

8. Who kept the ark for David and was blessed because of it?

9. Where did David take the ark, where he kept it in a tent?

10. In what city did Solomon finally put it, in its rightful place—the Most Holy Place?

ANSWERS

1. Bezalel. Exodus 37:1

2. The tribe of Levi. Deuteronomy 10:8

3. The Jordan River. Joshua 3:7

4. The Philistines. 1 Samuel 4:6-11

5. Dagon. 1 Samuel 5:2

6. Beth Shemesh. 1 Samuel 6:13

7. Abinadab. 1 Samuel 7:1-2

8. Obed-Edom. 2 Samuel 6:11

9. Zion, the City of David. 2 Samuel 6:16

10. Jerusalem. 1 Kings 18:1-6

? Who fell off his chair and died when he heard the ark had been stolen?

Eli. 1 Samuel 4:18

OFFER IT UP

In this multiple choice quiz, choose the kind of Old Testament offering that fits the description.

1. This one was given with a gesture.
   A. Burnt   B. Wave   C. Sin

2. This offering was burned outside the camp.
   A. Burnt   B. Guilt   C. Sin

3. Jacob poured this one on a stone pillar.
   A. Drink   B. Fellowship   C. Sin

4. "A pleasing aroma," describes this one.
   A. Drink   B. Burnt   C. Freewill

5. This one consists of flour, along with oil and incense.
   A. Fellowship   B. Grain   C. Guilt

6. Sometimes, this is prepared on a griddle.
   A. Burnt   B. Wave   C. Grain

7. This offering is burned as food, and includes fat from the internal organs.
   A. Freewill   B. Fellowship   C. Sin

8. If someone couldn't afford a lamb, he or she could offer two doves or pigeons for this offering.
   A. Sin   B. Guilt   C. Burnt

9. This offering is presented by someone who committed a violation unintentionally.
   A. Sin   B. Burnt   C. Guilt

10. This offering was kept burning all night.
    A. Sin   B. Fellowship   C. Burnt

ANSWERS

1. B. Wave. Exodus 29:24

2. C. Sin. Exodus 29:14

3. A. Drink. Genesis 35:14

4. B. Burnt. Exodus 29:18

5. B. Grain. Leviticus 2:1

6. C. Grain. Leviticus 2:5

7. B. Fellowship. Leviticus 3:6-11

8. A. Sin. Leviticus 5:7

9. C. Guilt. Leviticus 5:15

10. C. Burnt. Leviticus 6:9

The priest who offered a burnt offering for someone got to keep the hide. Leviticus 7:8

While King Elah was drunk at his friend's house, Zimre killed him and became the king of Israel. 1 Kings 16:10

Nothing in Solomon's house was made of silver because it wasn't worth much then. 1 Kings 10:21

The Philistines kept Israel from having blacksmiths because they were afraid they would make weapons.
1 Samuel 13:19

God once presented Himself to Elijah with a whisper, preceeded by a rock-shattering wind, an earthquake, and a fire. Now, that's an entrance. 1 Kings 19:11-12

? Bigthan and Teresh—what king did they plan to assassinate?

Xerxes. Esther 2:21

While Paul's ship was in danger during a storm, an angel told him that everybody on board would be fine, but the ship would be destroyed. Acts 27:22-24

Once when the disciples were on the Sea of Galilee, a storm kicked up. Out of nowhere they saw Jesus walking on the water, and when He climbed into the boat, they were all suddenly at the shore. John 6:21

When Solomon got old, he started worshiping false gods. So much for wisdom. 1 Kings 11:4

A FEW MORE BITS OF MISH

or is it Mash?

Abimelech found out that Sarah, whom he had taken into his house, was married because God warned him in a dream. Genesis 20:3

The Saducees didn't believe in the resurrection of the angels. The Pharisees did. Acts 23:8

Paul was stoned once, but not to death. 2 Corinthians 11:25

Solomon wrote 3,000 proverbs and 1,005 songs.
1 Kings 4:32

> **?** What covered the ark of the covenant whenever the Israelite camp moved?
> The shielding curtain. Numbers 4:5

When an Israelite stole something, he had to return it with an additional fifth of the value in order to make restitution. Leviticus 6:5

Noah sent out a dove three times to find land.
Genesis 8:9-12

The wave offering was called that because the Israelites waved it at God. Exodus 29:24

AWESOME Books for Kids!

Young Reader's Christian Library
Action, Adventure, and
Fun Reading!

This series for young readers ages 8 to 15 is action-packed, fast-paced, and Christ-centered! With exciting illustrations on every other page following the text, kids won't be able to put these books down! Over 100 illustrations per book. All books are paperbound.

The unique size (4-3/16" X 5-3/8") makes these books easy to take anywhere!

A Selection to Satisfy All Kids!

At the Back of the North Wind #13
Ben-Hur #7
Corrie ten Boom #3
David Livingstone #17
Dark Secrets of the Ouija, The #9
Elijah #15
Hudson Taylor #19
In His Steps #11
Jesus #4
Joseph #8
Miriam #20
Paul #12

Pilgrim's Progress, The #1
Robinson Crusoe #5
Ruth #6
Zaanan: The Fatal Limit
  #2 (Episode One)
Zaanan: The Dream of Delosar
  #6 (Episode Two)
Zaanan: The Ransom of
Renaissance
  #10 (Episode Three)
Zaanan: Conflict on Cada
Maylon
  #14 (Episode Four)

Available at Christian Book Stores Everywhere.
or order from:
Barbour and Company, Inc.
P.O. Box 719
Uhrichsville, Ohio 44683

$2.50 each retail, plus $1.00 for postage and handling per order.
Prices subject to change without notice.